Jon Scieszka's TRUCKTOWN on Reading Street

SPIN! SPIN!

PEARSON

Glenview, Illinois • Boston, Massachusetts • Chandler, Arizona
Shoreview, Minnesota • Upper Saddle River, New Jersey

Jack and Max sit on sand.

They spot Gabriella.

Will she yell go?

2

Gabriella will yell.

She said, "Get set! Go!"

Did Jack and Max go?

Spin! Spin! Spin!

Jack spun and spun.

But Jack did not go.

Spin! Spin! Spin!

Max spun and spun.

But Max did not go.

5

In a bit, Jack quit.

He did not spin.

"Max, you win," Jack said.

Win? Gabriella did not get it.

"Max did not go!" she said.

"Max can not win."

"Max did win!" said Jack.

"His hill of sand is big.

It is the best."